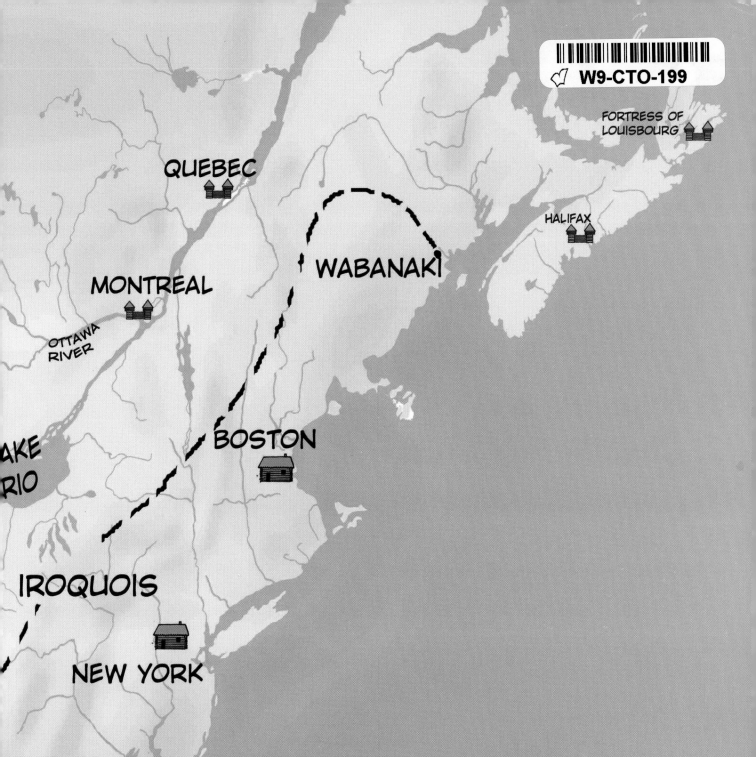

FORTRESS OF
LOUISBOURG

QUEBEC

HALIFAX

WABANAKI

MONTREAL

OTTAWA
RIVER

AKE
RIO

BOSTON

IROQUOIS

NEW YORK

THE FRENCH HAVE MOVED INTO THE GREAT LAKES REGION AND
ALONG THE ST. LAWRENCE AND OHIO RIVER VALLEYS. TO THE SOUTH
EAST, SMALL GROWING POCKETS OF ENGLISH AND EUROPEAN
SETTLEMENTS, KNOWN AS THE *13* BRITISH COLONIES, HAVE MOVED
INTO THE AREA AS WELL. THE ABORIGINAL COMMUNITIES REMAIN
AT PEACE WITH ALL THESE NEW NEIGHBOURS BUT THE GROWING
TENSIONS IN THE REGION ARE DISTURBING THAT PEACE AND HARMONY.
WHEREVER THEY GO, OUR HEROES, *RABBIT* AND *BEAR PAWS*,
ARE PLAYING GAMES ON THE NEIGHBOURS WITH VALUES THAT
HAVE SUSTAINED THEIR PEOPLE FOR LIFE.

BOOZHOO (WELCOME) PLEASE COME AND MEET THE FAMILY...

RABBIT, A PINT-SIZED HYPERACTIVE *12*-YEAR-OLD BOY, IS ALWAYS LOOKING FOR SOMETHING FUN AND INTERESTING TO DO. UNFORTUNATELY, RABBIT'S BOLD AND HEADSTRONG NATURE OFTEN GETS HIM INTO TROUBLE. RABBIT IS A LITTLE SMALL FOR HIS AGE BUT WHAT HE LACKS IN STATURE HE MAKES UP FOR IN SPEED WHEN HE RUNS.

BEAR PAWS IS A *10*-YEAR-OLD BOY, A 'LITTLE GIANT' WHO LIKES TO SPEND TIME WITH HIS BROTHER, RABBIT, PLAYING JOKES ON PEOPLE AND ANIMALS. HOWEVER, THESE PRANKS USUALLY BACKFIRE, AND THE BROTHERS OFTEN LEARN THEIR LESSONS THE HARD WAY. BEAR PAWS HAS ALREADY REACHED THE HEIGHT OF A FULL-GROWN MALE, AND CLAIMS TO HAVE THE STRENGTH OF TEN GRIZZLY BEARS, HOWEVER, HE IS NAÏVE AND HAS THE GULLIBILITY TO MATCH. THANKFULLY, HE ALSO USES HIS GIFTS AND TRICKS FOR THE GOOD OF THE PEOPLE.

CLOVER BLOSSOM, ADOPTIVE MOTHER OF BEAR PAWS AND RABBIT, HAS HER HANDS FULL TRYING TO KEEP HER BOYS OUT OF TROUBLE. HER EYESIGHT IS NOT WHAT IT USED TO BE, THOUGH HER POWERFUL VOICE IS AS LOUD AS EVER. ALTHOUGH THE BOYS CAN DRIVE HER CRAZY, SHE LOVES THEM WITH ALL HER HEART - SO MUCH SO, IN FACT, THAT SHE RARELY SUSPECTS THEM OF ANY WRONGDOING.

GREY STONE IS THE ADOPTIVE FATHER OF BEAR PAWS AND RABBIT AND IS ALSO THE VILLAGE MEDICINE MAN. GREY STONE HAS MANY GIFTS AND POWERS. IT ISN'T ALWAYS A GOOD IDEA TO ASK FOR HIS HELP, SINCE HIS MIND OFTEN APPEARS TO BE SOMEWHERE ELSE, MAKING PEOPLE THINK HE'S A LITTLE CRAZY. ONE OF HIS GIFTS IS SPIRIT (CHEEBY) POWDER THAT TRANSFORMS PEOPLE INTO ANIMALS.

...AND NOW ON TO THE ADVENTURES!!!

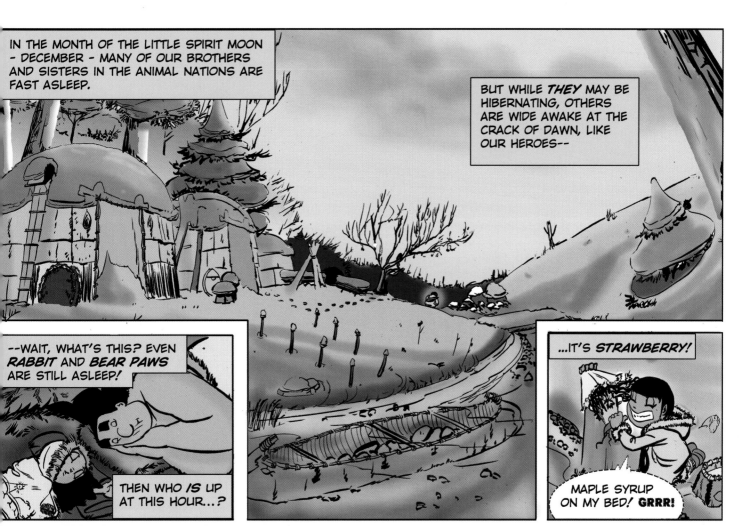

IN THE MONTH OF THE LITTLE SPIRIT MOON - DECEMBER - MANY OF OUR BROTHERS AND SISTERS IN THE ANIMAL NATIONS ARE FAST ASLEEP.

BUT WHILE *THEY* MAY BE HIBERNATING, OTHERS ARE WIDE AWAKE AT THE CRACK OF DAWN, LIKE OUR HEROES--

--WAIT, WHAT'S THIS? EVEN *RABBIT* AND *BEAR PAWS* ARE STILL ASLEEP!

THEN WHO *IS* UP AT THIS HOUR...?

...IT'S *STRAWBERRY!*

MAPLE SYRUP ON MY BED! **GRRR!**

THAT WATER MUST BE *FREEZING!* NOW WHY WOULD STRAWBERRY HAVE TO WASH HER HAIR SO *EARLY?*

RABBIT! ARRRGHHH!

ONLY *HE* WOULD HAVE COVERED MY PILLOW IN MAPLE SYRUP.

HOW CAN I GET THE LAST LAUGH ON RABBIT...?

GIIBOT! GOOD MORNING TO YOU!

CAREFUL WHERE YOU ROLL, GIRL, OR ELSE YOU'LL--

--SMASH MY BREAKFAST... OF APPLES...

HMM...

RABBIT! BEAR PAWS! **WAKE UP!!**

HUNH...?

LOOK! IT'S THE *FIRST SNOW* OF THE SEASON!

IT SNOWED! *IT SNOWED!!*

OBOYOBOY! COME ON LET'S GO! I BET IT SNOWED A WHOLE...

...TWO FEET...

SPLURCH!

MUSHY APPLES... HA...IN MUKLUKS... HAHAHAHAHAHA!!!

I GUESS I DESERVED THAT...

ENJOYING THE FRUIT OF YOUR LABOUR?

HAHAHAHAHAHAHA AHAHAHAHAHHA HAHAHAHAAHA!!

LATER...

RABBIT! ABOUT TIME YOU CLEANED UP!

IT'S TIME TO GO ON AN ADVENTURE!

YOU MEAN THE KIND OF ADVENTURE WHERE I END UP EATING MUD, OR MY HAIR GETS BURNT OFF, OR--

--OH! *THIS* KIND OF ADVENTURE!

HAHAHAHAHAHAHAHAH AHAHAHAHAHAHAHAH!!

OH, WHAT'S THE *USE*? I'LL *NEVER* CATCH HIM. HE'S JUST TOO FAST!

CHEER UP, STRAWBERRY. YOU MAY NOT BE ABLE TO OUTRUN A QUICK RABBIT, BUT THERE ARE OTHER WAYS TO CATCH ONE! FOLLOW ME...

A SHORT TIME LATER.

FIRST, FIND AN AREA WHERE THE RABBIT LIKES TO TRAVEL.

THEN, USE BAIT THAT WILL ATTRACT THE RABBIT - LIKE *PEMMICAN* *.

*HIGH ENERGY FOOD.

ADD THAT PEPPER I ASKED YOU TO BRING...AND NOW WE WAIT, LIKE *NANABOOZHOO* ONCE DID.

NANABOOZHOO HAD A SCORE TO SETTLE WITH RABBIT, *TOO*?

NO... WELL, PROBABLY NOT...

"LONG AGO, NANABOOZHOO NEEDED TO CATCH IMPOSSIBLE PREY. FOR HE WAS HUNGRIER THAN HE HAD EVER BEEN..."

"...AND A GROUP OF *DUCKS* WERE HIS ONLY CHANCE AT A MEAL."

"BUT EVEN THAT CHANCE WAS SMALL. HE KNEW FROM EXPERIENCE THAT THE QUICK DUCKS WOULD FLY AWAY THE MOMENT HE APPROACHED THEM."

"AND PREVIOUS ATTEMPTS TO SNEAK UP ON THEM HAD CAUSED NANABOOZHOO MUCH DANGER AND HUMILIATION..."

"...BUT THAT'S A STORY FOR ANOTHER TIME."

"STILL VERY HUNGRY AND OUT OF IDEAS, NANABOOZHOO KNEW HE HAD TO GET HIS MIND OFF OF HIS HUNGER. SO HE PLAYED HIS DRUM AND CHANTED SOFTLY."

"HE STARTED TO FEEL BETTER QUICKLY, THANKS TO THE MUSIC. AND HE THOUGHT, IF HE BEGAN TO SING, THAT *KITCHI-MANITOU* MIGHT TAKE PITY ON HIM."

"HE BEGAN TO SING. AND SOON, HE BEGAN TO DANCE. AND AS HE GREW MORE CHEERFUL, HIS SINGING GREW LOUDER..."

"...AND HE ATTRACTED ATTENTION."

"BEFORE LONG, NANABOOZHOO RECEIVED AN UNEXPECTED VISITOR..."

EXCUSE ME?

ARE YOU DANCING? MAY I DANCE, TOO?

YOU? SERIOUSLY? YOUR FEET ARE FLAT! DO YOU EVEN KNOW *HOW* TO DANCE?

WELL... I CAN LEARN...

HMM...VERY WELL. DO AS I DO.

"THEY BOTH DANCED AND SANG, THE LITTLE DUCK QUACKING WITH HAPPINESS."

"AND THEIR DANCING CAUGHT THE EYES OF THE OTHERS..."

"...AND SOON, NANABOOZHOO HAD THE ATTENTION OF EVERY DUCK ON THE LAKE. HE WAS AMAZED - AND STILL *HUNGRY.* SO HE DEVISED A PLAN..."

BROTHERS AND SISTERS, LET ME TEACH YOU A *NEW* DANCE. IT IS CALLED THE "CLOSE YOUR EYES" DANCE, AND IT IS THE MOST FUN OF ALL!

WOW!

COOL!

FIRST, YOU MUST GATHER LOTS OF WOOD FOR A BONFIRE.

NOW, DANCE AS I DO. YOU MUST CHANT LOUDLY, AND *DO NOT* OPEN YOUR EYES! IF YOU OPEN YOUR EYES, THE DANCE WILL *END.*

OH, NO!

"THE DANCE BEGAN AND THE DUCKS DANCED AND CHANTED AS LOUDLY AS THEY COULD. IT WAS SUCH A *RUCKUS* THAT NANABOOZHOO'S DRUM COULD NOT BE HEARD."

"SO IT WAS VERY EASY FOR HIM TO APPROACH EACH BLIND DUCK, ONE BY ONE..."

URK!

"...AND SOON, HE HAD ENOUGH FOOD COOKING ON THE FIRE TO SATISFY HIS INCREDIBLE HUNGER!"

"NANABOOZHOO WAS AMAZED: HE'D BEEN ABLE TO OUTSMART THE DUCKS THROUGH *PATIENCE.*"

YAWN

I'M SURE NANABOOZHOO WAS HUNGRY, BUT DID HE REALLY NEED TO EAT *ALL* OF THOSE DUCKS?

ACTUALLY... NANABOOZHOO WAS SO SATISFIED THAT HE TOOK A *NAP*. AND HE AWOKE LATER TO FIND THE DUCKS *TOO BURNT* TO EAT.

WELL, THAT DOESN'T FILL ME WITH CONFIDENCE...

LOOK!

--AND THEN I SAID "I BET I CAN*!*" BUT HE SAID "I BET YOU CAN'T*!*" SO THEN I-- *HEY*, WHAT'S *THIS*??

RABBIT, YOU DON'T KNOW WHERE THAT PEMMICAN HAS BEEN*!*

SURE I DO! IT'S BEEN *RIGHT HERE*, WAITING FOR ME*!*

JUST DON'T BITE OFF MORE THAN YOU CAN CHEW.

MM-*MMM!* LET ME JUST TAKE IN--

--THE AROMA--A-- AH--*AAAAAH*--

YOU OK RABBIT?

YEAH, MY NOSE TICKLES.

AAAAHHHHHH

WELL, THAT WAS... UNEXPECTED.

HEY, I AM *BEAR PAWS*, AND THIS IS MY BROTHER, *RABBIT*. WE'RE VERY SORRY FOR RUINING YOUR MEAL. IT WAS AN *ACCIDENT*.

WELL, I AM *TALL BEAR*, A HEALER FROM THE SOUTH. PERHAPS YOU'VE HEARD OF ME?

UH...

WELL...I AM VERY WELL-KNOWN IN *MOST* AREAS!

NOPE.

I HAVE SPENT MY ENTIRE LIFE STUDYING MEDICINES AND HEALING.

BUT I NEVER LEARNED TO *HUNT*. THAT'S WHY I GROW SO *HUNGRY* WHEN I TRAVEL ALONE.

WEIRD. OUR DAD *GREY STONE* KNOWS HOW TO HUNT - AND HE'S A VERY TALENTED HEALER. HE HELPED TO CREATE A POWERFUL MEDICINE CALLED SPIRIT POWDER!

PLEASE EXPLAIN THIS "SPIRIT POWDER"... AND *GREY STONE*.

UH...HE'S OUR *FATHER*, AND AN AWESOME HEALER!

HAH! I DOUBT HE'S A BETTER HEALER THAN I.

OH YEAH? HIS SPIRIT POWDER IS SO POWERFUL THAT IT CAN TURN *PEOPLE* INTO *ANIMALS*--

--AND I BET *YOU* CAN'T DO THAT!

NO, I CAN'T. BUT NOW I KNOW HOW YOU CAN REPAY ME FOR RUINING MY DINNER-- YOU WILL TEACH ME HOW TO *MAKE* THIS SPIRIT POWDER!

SURE, WE'LL TEACH YOU HOW TO MAKE SPIRIT POWDER--

HOLD THAT THOUGHT.

WE *CAN'T* TEACH HIM THAT! *THINK* FOR A MOMENT!

BEAR, SOMETIMES BEING HUNGRY FEELS LIKE THE WORST THING IN THE WORLD. WE OWE HIM FOR RUINING HIS MEAL.

THEN LET'S SHARE SOME FOOD FROM OUR *VILLAGE.*

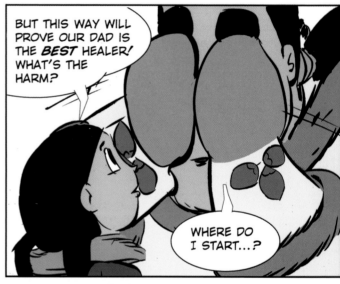

BUT THIS WAY WILL PROVE OUR DAD IS THE *BEST* HEALER! WHAT'S THE HARM?

WHERE DO I START...?

COME HERE, LITTLE SQUIRREL!

I DON'T *TRUST* TALL BEAR.

WHY NOT? HE'S A LITTLE WEIRD, BUT AREN'T WE ALL?

HEY! COME BACK!

I DON'T KNOW. IT FEELS LIKE HE'S...*HIDING* SOMETHING.

LIKE *WHAT?*

GET *OUT HERE!*

RRRRAAAAAAAIIII!

LIKE *INCREDIBLE STRENGTH?*

WE SHOULD RUN AWAY. *FAST.*

14

BOYS! WHERE ARE YOU GOING?

EEP!

ULP!

NOWHERE! JUST, UH, HEADED TO THE FIRST *INGREDIENT* OF THE *SPIRIT POWDER!*

HOORAY! I'M SO VERY *EXCITED!*

PSST! RABBIT, DO YOU EVEN *KNOW* THE INGREDIENTS?

OF COURSE NOT! BUT WE'VE GOT TO KEEP THIS GUY BUSY... AND *AWAY* FROM THE *VILLAGE!*

HOW LONG CAN WE LEAD HIM ON A *GOOSE CHASE?*

I DON'T KNOW... UNTIL HE LOSES INTEREST?

WELL? WHERE'S THE FIRST INGREDIENT?

ER... YOU SEE...

IT'S NOT THAT SIMPLE. BEFORE YOU CAN BEGIN, YOU MUST PURIFY YOUR *SPIRIT, MIND, BODY* AND *EMOTIONS.*

AND YOU MUST DO *EXACTLY* AS WE SAY, OR IT WON'T WORK.

VERY WELL. BUT YOU HAD BETTER TELL ME THE *TRUTH*...OR *ELSE!*

AH, YES! THE *TRUTH!* HA-HA -HA! OF COURSE! HA HA...HEH...

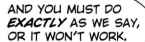

IN ORDER TO MAKE SPIRIT POWDER, YOU MUST FIRST BECOME *TRULY PURE* BY UNDERGOING SEVERAL *TRIALS.*

FIRST, YOU MUST DISCARD YOUR CLOTHING, AND WEAR ONLY NATURE'S GIFT OF *MUD.*

THIS HOT SPRING IS WHERE DAD STARTS WHEN MAKING THE SPIRIT POWDER.

NOW, YOU MUST MEDITATE ON THE BACKS OF SLEEPING PORCUPINES WHILE FOCUSING ON THE ANIMAL YOU WANT TO TURN INTO.

NEXT, CARRY THIS IRON STONE UP THAT MOUNTAIN, AND WAIT FOR THE THUNDER BIRD TO SPEAK TO YOU.

DID THE THUNDER BIRD SPEAK WITH YOU?

YES... SHE DID. IT... WAS... VERY SHOCKING TO... HEAR HER... VOICE.

NOW, ARE YOU READY TO LOOK FOR THE INGREDIENTS?

YES. I FEEL AS PURE AS THE DAY I WAS BORN.

GOOD, TO COLLECT THE FIRST INDGREDIENT. YOUR HANDS MUST BE BURNT BY FLINT STONE TO BE STRONG TO COLLECT THE BARK FROM AN EAGLE'S NEST. ARE YOU READY?

READY.

OUCH!OUCH! OUCH!OUCH!OUCH!
OUCH!OUCH !OUCH!OUCH!OUCH
OUCH!OUC H!OUCH!OUCH!OU
OUCH! OUC H!OUCH!OUCH!O
OUCH! OUCH!OUCH!O
OUCH! OUCH!OUCH!O
OUCH! OUCH!OUCH!
OUCH! OUCH!OUCH!
OUCH! OUCH!
OUC H!OU
OUC H!OUCH
OUC H!OUCH
OU CH!OUCH
OU CH!OUCH!OUCH
OU CH!OUCH
OU CH!OUCH!

LET ME SEE YOUR HANDS. GOOD, YOU ARE READY.

NOW, CLIMB THIS TREE FOR THE BARK OF THE EAGLE'S NEST.

YES, I DID IT!!

OH... OH... HELLO...

aaaaaaaa

WAY TO GO, YOU DID IT!

GOOD JOB!

THUMP!

ON... TO THE... NEXT... INGREDIENT!

I THINK I LOST THAT EAGLE SOMEWHERE DURING MY FALL. THIS IS *EVERYTHING*, RIGHT?

YEP*!* WELL, *ALMOST* EVERYTHING.

ALMOST? ALMOST??

YES...*!* THERE'S *ONE* INGREDIENT LEFT!

THE ROOTS OF A *BLUE ROSE:* THE RAREST FLOWER OF ALL*!* IT COULD BE *ANYWHERE* IN THIS FOREST.

A FLOWER? THAT'S *IT?*

WHOOPEEE!

WHAT IF HE ACTUALLY *FINDS ONE* IN THE SNOW?

OH, DON'T WORRY. BLUE ROSES DON'T EVEN *EXIST.*

TALL BEAR IS LOOKING FOR A FLOWER THAT *DOESN'T EXIST?* THAT'S FUNNY!

AT SOME POINT HE'LL *HAVE* TO GIVE UP AND GO HOME!

WANT TO HAVE SOME FUN WHILE WE WAIT?

TAKE SOME OF THIS *SPIRIT POWDER...*

NOW THINK OF SOMETHING SMALL AND NIMBLE, LIKE *SQUIRRELS...*

POOF

WE'RE...WE'RE *SQUIRRELS!*

I'M JUST SURPRISED NOTHING WENT WRONG...*!*

ISN'T THAT WHAT YOU WANTED?

THERE HE IS!

MAYBE HERE? NO... MAYBE HERE?

NO... MAYBE--

HEY RABBIT, BET YOU CAN'T HIT TALL BEAR WITH THIS ACORN.

OH, YEAH?

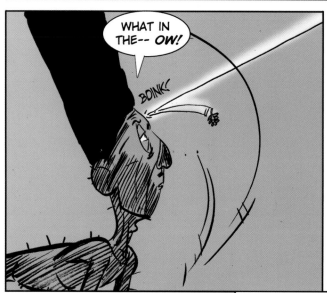

WHAT IN THE-- OW!

BOINK!

PESKY RODENTS! COME DOWN HERE AND BE MY DINNER, OR LEAVE ME ALONE!

HEE HEE!

HA HA! THE LOOK ON HIS FACE!

YEAH...HE LOOKS PRETTY MAD AT US.

DON'T WORRY. STANDING BEAR COULDN'T RECOGNIZE US. AND EVEN IF HE DID, THERE'S NO WAY HE COULD REACH US!

CRACK!

WAAAAA

OK, I DID NOT CONSIDER THAT.

MOM, YOU'RE **FRIENDS** WITH THIS GUY?

NO.

YES!

ER, WELL...WE HAVEN'T SEEN EACH OTHER IN **MANY YEARS.** NOT SINCE WE WERE **YOUNG**...

"...LIVING IN THE SAME VILLAGE. TALL BEAR AND I SAW QUITE A **LOT** OF ONE ANOTHER."

"YES, I WAS QUITE THE **YOUNG HEARTTHROB.**"

"NO, YOU WERE **LAZY** AND **DIRECTIONLESS,** ALWAYS NEGLECTING YOUR DUTIES TO THE VILLAGE HEALER..."

"...LEAVING ALL THE WORK TO HIS **OTHER** HELPER -- GREY STONE."

"AH YES, I REMEMBER **GREY STONE.** AND I REMEMBER HIM **STEALING** YOU AWAY FROM ME."

"HE STOLE **NOTHING.** I SAW HIS STRONG AND KIND SPIRIT, COMPARED IT TO YOUR **SELFISHNESS**..."

"...AND I MADE MY **DECISION.**"

>SNIFF<...I REGRET YOUR DECISION... AND I ALSO REGRET **FAILING** IN MY ATTEMPTS TO... **GET EVEN** WITH GREY STONE.

WAIT...WHAT ARE YOU SAYING?

BACK AWAY, RABBIT. THIS MAN WAS **EXPELLED** FROM OUR VILLAGE FOR A REASON.

PLEASE BE ON YOUR WAY, TALL BEAR. YOU HAVE NO *BUSINESS* HERE.

OH, BUT I *DO.* YOU SEE, YOUR BOYS *PROMISED* ME SOMETHING...

...THE SECRET TO GREY STONE'S *SPIRIT POWDER.*

OH, *REALLY?*

WELL, I'M AFRAID MY BOYS CANNOT KEEP THAT PROMISE.

MY, CLOVER BLOSSOM, YOU'RE SO *CUTE* WHEN YOU'RE STERN.

BUT WHAT AM I TO DO? IF YOU ALL INSIST ON BEING UNHELPFUL, I'LL HAVE TO VISIT GREY STONE *MYSELF.*

PERHAPS HE CAN HELP ME... I AM *SO VERY* HUNGRY!

NO... YOU'VE BECOME A *BEAR WALKER,* HAVEN'T YOU?

YOU HAVE *NO IDEA* WHAT I'VE HAD TO DO TO SURVIVE! I CAN'T *HUNT* AND I CAN'T *COOK...*

...SO I HAVE TO *MAKE DO* WITH WHAT I GET... EVEN IF IT'S *RAW MEAT!*

WAIT! HOLD ON A SECOND!

IF YOU THINK YOU'RE SO GREAT, THEN I...I HEREBY CHALLENGE YOU TO A *RACE!*

AND IF I WIN, YOU HAVE TO LEAVE US ALONE *FOREVER!*

A *RACE?* HA! IF I WON, WHAT COULD YOU GIVE ME THAT'S BETTER THAN *SPIRIT POWDER?*

UM...A DELICIOUS MEAL?

THE SATISFACTION OF VICTORY?

RABBIT WILL BE YOUR PERSONAL HELPER.

WILL *NOT!*

AS I SUSPECTED...YOU HAVE NOTHING I WANT. NOW, EXCUSE ME WHILE I GO *DESTROY* YOUR VILLAGE--

WAIT. THERE IS *ONE* THING.

ME. IF YOU WIN, AND SPARE OUR VILLAGE...I WILL GIVE YOU *MY HAND.*

REALLY...!

HUH??

MOM!

BUT YOU CAN'T--! YOU SHOULDN'T...

DON'T WORRY, RABBIT. IT'S MY DECISION.

BUT--

I ACCEPT YOUR CHALLENGE!!

BUT--

FINALLY, MY CHANCE TO WIN BACK THE BEAUTIFUL CLOVER BLOSSOM!

NOW, YOU NEVER DEFINED THE *TERMS* OF THE RACE... SO I WILL!

BUT--!!

WE WILL RACE IN ONE HOUR.

I SHALL EXPLORE THE AREA AND DETERMINE A *COURSE* FOR OUR RACE!

MOM...YOU DON'T *HAVE* TO DO THIS. WE'LL FIGURE *SOMETHING* OUT.

NO. *BEAR WALKERS* ARE HEALERS WHO USE THEIR GIFTS FOR THE WRONG REASONS AND ARE NOT TO BE TAKEN LIGHTLY. WE HAVE NO WAY TO *DEFEAT* HIM OR *EXPEL* HIM FROM OUR LANDS....

...SO, IF I MUST, I WILL *GLADLY* GIVE UP MY FREEDOM FOR THE SAFETY OF MY FRIENDS AND FAMILY.

IT IS SIMPLY THE *RIGHT THING* TO DO.

OK! I CAN *HELP!*

UH...NO, THAT'S FINE, PLEASE--

I, UH, HAVE TO GO *PRACTICE!*

I'LL HELP YOU WITH *SIT-UPS* AND *SQUATS* AND EVERYTHING--

I DON'T *WANT* YOU TO!

OH, I GET IT NOW. WELL...

>SNIFF<

THERE IS *ONE* THING I CAN DO.

...MEEGWETCH.

24

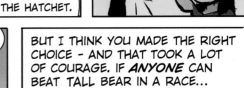

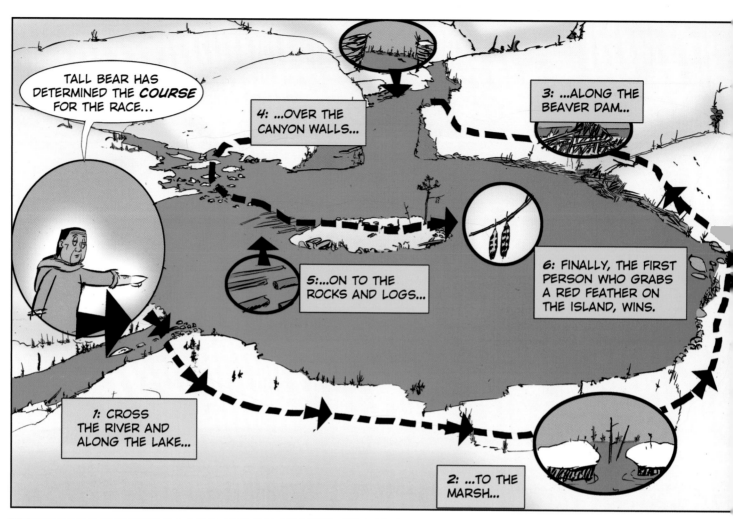

TALL BEAR HAS DETERMINED THE *COURSE* FOR THE RACE...

4: ...OVER THE CANYON WALLS...

3: ...ALONG THE BEAVER DAM...

5: ...ON TO THE ROCKS AND LOGS...

6: FINALLY, THE FIRST PERSON WHO GRABS A RED FEATHER ON THE ISLAND, WINS.

1: CROSS THE RIVER AND ALONG THE LAKE...

2: ...TO THE MARSH...

" NOW REMEMBER RABBIT, THE RACE WILL START HERE ALONG THE LAKE..."

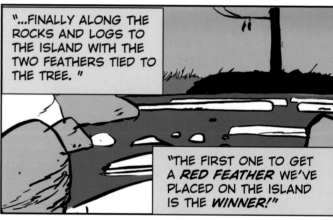

"...FINALLY ALONG THE ROCKS AND LOGS TO THE ISLAND WITH THE TWO FEATHERS TIED TO THE TREE. "

"THE FIRST ONE TO GET A *RED FEATHER* WE'VE PLACED ON THE ISLAND IS THE *WINNER!*"

THE COURSE DOESN'T LOOK TOO HARD. HEAR THAT, MOM? DON'T YOU WORRY, I'LL WIN IN *NO TIME!*

HA!

YOU MAY BE FAST, BUT YOU'RE TOO *CLUMSY* TO HANDLE THOSE STEPPING STONES. *NOBODY* IS MORE SURE-FOOTED THAN I!

ENOUGH TALK! TIME TO PUT YOUR *FEET* WHERE YOUR *MOUTH* IS!

3...2...1...

YES! I DID IT! I WON!

I'M THE--

CHEATER!

I HAVE SPENT *WINTERS** WALKING PATHS ONLY FEW COULD TRAVEL, OVER MOUNTAINS AND RIVER RAPIDS. NOT *ONCE* DID I EVER SLIP OR FALL.

THERE'S A FIRST TIME FOR EVERYTHING... RIGHT?

* YEARS

YOU CHEATED BY USING YOUR SPIRIT POWDER, DIDN'T YOU? TO MAKE SURE I'D *LOSE* THE RACE!

UH, IT DOESN'T REALLY *WORK* LIKE THAT.

I'M SORRY, TALL BEAR! I CAN'T SAY FOR CERTAIN WHY YOU SLIPPED AND FELL. NONE OF US ARE PERFECT. YOU *LOST*, FAIR AND SQUARE!

LIAR!

THE ONLY THING LIARS ARE GOOD FOR IS DINNER!!

29

C'MON! WE HAVE TO HURRY!

WHOOPS!

SPOOOSHHH!

OH, SO I CAN'T CHEAT, BUT IT'S OK FOR YOU TO TURN INTO A GIANT AND EAT YOUR RIVAL??

YES. AS PUNISHMENT. YOU, AND THEN YOUR ENTIRE VILLAGE!

HEY, YOU! MONSTER!

WHY DON'T YOU EAT ME FIRST?

STRAWBERRY! NO!

"STRAWBERRY"? HMM......PERHAPS I COULD TRY A FRUIT APPETIZER FIRST!

HEY!

TIME FOR MY FIRST COURSE!

FINALLY! DINNER TIME!

HOLD ON...

...DON'T YOU WANT SOME PEPPER WITH THAT?

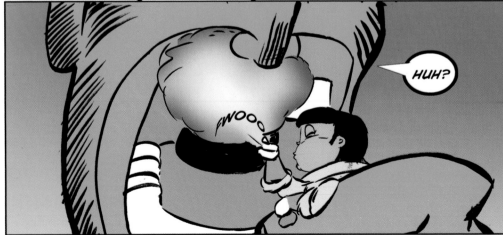

FWOOO

HUH?

WHAAA... AAA...AAAHHH...

WOW, THAT IS SOME SNEEZE!

I'LL SAY...

EWW! MONSTER SNOT! THIS IS GONNA TAKE *FOREVER* TO CLEAN OFF...

MAYBE SO, RABBIT, BUT *LOOK!*

TALL BEAR... HE'S *LONG GONE!*

YOU'RE RIGHT!

YOU'RE *SAFE*, MOM!

MEEGWETCH, RABBIT!

IT WASN'T *JUST* ME...

...MEEGWETCH, STRAWBERRY, FOR SAVING ALL OF US. AND FOR, UH, WHAT YOU SAID EARLIER... YOU KNOW...

WHATEVER. LET'S GO, GIIBOT!

I DO *NOT* UNDERSTAND GIRLS!

32